© SUSAETA EDICIONES, S.A.
Editor in Chief: Ana Doblado
Original Spanish Text: A-rredondo / Susaeta editorial team
Book Design and Illustrations: A-rredondo
Production: Antonia Maria Martinez
Art Editor: José de Haro

ISBN: 978-0-7097-1776-8
© 2007 Brown Watson, English Edition
Reprinted 2008

Design and illustrations
A-rredondo

English edition translated from
the Spanish and edited by
Maureen Spurgeon

# Amazing Animals

Brown Watson

# Meet the dinosaurs!

Dinosaurs were some of the largest animals to ever live on Earth. Finding enough to eat without being eaten themselves was quite a problem!

**Can you find 3 animals which did not exist in the age of dinosaurs?**

The Tyrannosaurus was the largest of the carnivores (meat-eaters). It grew up to 15 metres in length and weighed 7 tonnes. Find 5.

The **Eoraptor** is the most primitive (earliest) dinosaur yet discovered. See if you can find 4 more!

The **Brachiosaurus** was the largest of all dinosaurs, weighing up to 77 tonnes and with a maximum height of 11 metres. You can easily find 5!

The Diplodocus was the longest dinosaur – 27 metres. Its tail ended in a dangerous whip. Can you see 4?

6

# High flyers, high jumpers!

Sometimes we think of animals as those living on land, like us. But, of course, there are many which live high above the ground, or which fly across the skies, beautiful creatures of many different types.

Donkeys cannot fly! But there are 4 hidden here for you to find!

The gazelle has no wings – but it can jump to a height of 3.5 metres! Now you 'jump to it' and find 7!

The Bald Eagle has good eyesight – and its nest is one of the largest, at least 3 metres in diameter! Find 8 eagles.

This antelope can clear a length of more than 9 metres in one jump. Find 5 antelopes, and you can jump for joy!

There are thousands of species of birds in the world, of all shapes and sizes and in many colours. Some species are still being discovered. How many can you see here?

The Common Goose mates with just one partner, and they stay together for life. See if you can find 14.

9

# European animals

In Europe, there are as many wild animals as there are people! We must do all we can to look after and protect them.

**There are 3 animals from Africa here! Can you see them?**

The Iberian Lynx from Spain and Portugal is almost extinct. Now, it is a protected species. Can you count 9?

The pygmy shrew is the smallest mammal in the world. Be careful not to tread on any of the 10 shrews to be found here!

The Great Bustard is the largest flying, bird not only in Europe, but also in the world. Because of its size, it stays mostly on the ground. Can you see if there are 11 here?

The common snail is one of the slowest-moving animals. Find 5 which have escaped!

Did you know that the dragonfly is the fastest insect? It can fly at a speed of up to 80 kilometres an hour. Are you fast enough to see 5?

At certain times, whole communities of lemmings leap to their deaths, drowning in lakes and rivers. It is thought that they do this to control their numbers. Here, there are just 9 to find.

11

# Woodland creatures

It would be impossible to see all the creatures which live in a wood at one glance. Birds, frogs, deer, badgers, hedgehogs, squirrels, rabbits, foxes... there are so many.

The Arctic Swan is the bird with the most feathers – more than 25,200!
Can you work out how many feathers the 8 swans in this picture have between them?

Swooping dwon on its prey, the Peregrine Falcon reaches the same speed as a Formula 1 racing car – 300 kilometres an hour! You will need to be quick to find 4!

Can you see?
There are 3 polar animals to be found.

When a **hedgehog** senses danger, it rolls itself up into a spiny ball to protect itself.
Can you find 7 hedgehogs?

Of all **porcupines** the Crested Porcupine has the longest spines. These can grow up to 50 cm! Be careful of those spines when you search for 4!

12

A badger digs burrows (or 'setts') of up to 20 metres deep, where many generations live together. 7 badgers have come out of their sett, ready for you to find.

Did you know that a crow can live for up to 80 years? It will not take you as long to find 8!

# Asia, the roof of the world

Asia is often called 'the roof of the world' because it has the highest mountains on Earth, including Mount Everest, which every mountaineer dreams of climbing. It is 8,848 metres high!

The Ibex can live at heights of more than 5,500 metres. Look high up to find 5.

To combat the cold, the Japanese Macaque will submerge itself up to its neck in the warm Asiatic waters. Can you find 12 macaques?

How have 3 large cats climbed up here?

The Siberian Tiger is the largest cat in the world, growing up to 2 metres – not counting the tail! Being so huge, you can easily find 7!

The Saiga is an antelope with a nose like a snout. This warms the air which it breathes in. Can you find 11?

The Chinese Panda has the unfortunate distinction of being the animal which is most at risk of extinction throughout the world. Here you can find 7 protected pandas.

15

# Rivers and lakes

You don't need to go to Africa to see an elephant, or to the largest oceans to see a blue whale... There are many record-breaking animals in our rivers and lakes!

Among all these insects, there are 4 ladybirds to find.

The Goliath Frog is a true giant among insects – 87 cm in length and weighing more than 3.5 kilograms! See if you can count 6!

The Piranha is the fiercest fish in the world. A shoal has been k to attack large animals. Take care, there are 5 lurking about.

The Archer Fish has a magnificent aim! It can hit an insect at more than 2 metres by shooting water from its mouth. Can you find 5?

One of the smallest reptiles is the Dwarf Gecko, measuring only 2 cm, not counting the tail. The suction pads on its feet enable it to cling to glass and to move on a ceiling. You will find yourself up against a brick wall if you cannot find 6!

The Mudskipper Fish can live out of water for several hours. Can you find 7?

The Queen Alexandra butterfly is the largest in the world, with a wingspan of more than 26 cm! There are 7 to find!

Not only is the Stick Insect the largest insect (up to 40 cm long!) it is also unbeatable at hiding itself, thanks to its shape and colour. See if you can find 5!

# Geniuses at camouflage

It is not always easy to see the animals shown on these pages. Each one is a genius at camouflage, hiding themselves so that they blend in with their surroundings.

Can you find 5 budgerigars which are lost here?

Geometrid caterpillars look very similar to twigs. Don't break any while trying to find 5!

Frogs and toads can also assume a range of colourings in order to hide themselves. It may be difficult to find 11!

There are some butterflies and moths which can camouflage themselves on petals and tree-trunks. Can you find 11 hidden here?

18

This may look like a petal – but do not be fooled. It is an insect. There are 5 more to find!

# Animals in Africa

With so many animals in Africa, it is not surprising that there are lots of record-breakers! Here, are just a few examples...

**Can you find one polar animal and one farm animal?**

The tallest animal is the giraffe. A male can grow to a height of 6 metres. Can you see 6?

The most intelligent mammal is the chimpanzee. If you are clever, you can find 10!

The cheetah is the fastest mammal on Earth, reaching speeds of more than 100 kilometres per hour. Get moving and you can find 4!

As well as having an excellent memory, the elephant is the heaviest land mammal, weighing up to 7 tonnes. There are 9 to find here.

The ostrich is the largest bird and female ostriches lay the largest eggs! Find 5 ostriches.

# In the jungle

There are so many animals living in the world's jungles, and every kind has its own record. Here are just a few.

The Golden Arrow Frog is so poisonous that the venom from just one could kill 1500 people. Don't touch one – but find 8!

4 hens have got lost in the thicket. Find them before they get eaten!

The sloth is small and lazy! It spends two hours each day eating, and the rest of the time it sleeps. Don't you go to sleep when there are 7 to find!

The cries of the Howler Monkey can be heard at distances of more than 12 kilometres. Can you find 6?

The hummingbird holds 5 records! It is the smallest bird, it has the fewest feathers, the smallest nest, the fastest-moving wings, and it lays the smallest eggs... Find 8 hummingbirds!

The Phyllomedusa Leaf Frog is the smallest frog in the world, measuring only 1.2 cm. Compare this to the length of a pencil – then find 6!

The smallest monkey is the Pygmy Teetee. Its body measures only 15 cm. Can you find another 9?

# North America

Canada and the United States are huge countries, each contains many differents types of territory. Some parts are very cold all year round. Others have enormous forests, high mountains, great lakes, vast prairies and great deserts. Each territory is home to a variety of wild animals.

**There are 4 African animals here by mistake. Where are they?**

Did you know that the elk grows to a height of 2.5 metres and a width of 3 metres? Its antlers can grow to a record-breaking 2.29 metres. With those antlers, it is easy to find 6 elks.

The Musk Ox is the largest herbivore (plant-eater). Its fur can grow to a length of 1 metre.

Can you find 7 Musk Oxen?

One of the fastest mammals in North America is the Pronghorn Antelope. It can reach speeds of up to 80 kilometres an hour. Find 11!

24

The Red Lynx is less than 1 metre in length, but it can capture a fully-grown deer. See if you can find 6!

The Swallowtail Butterfly is a great traveller. It can cover over 3000 kilometres from Canada to Mexico! Get after it and find another 15!

The Blue Jay is a great planter of trees, burying seeds after it has finished eating! Can you find 5?

25

# Under the sea

Huge parts of our planet are covered by seas and oceans. It is here that we meet the most amazing animals. Here are just a few.

First, you can collect up gold ingots, if you like!

The Killer Whale is both fierce and intelligent, breaking through ice to capture and kill seals for food. Here, there are 5 to find.

The Moon Fish sets a record by laying 30 million eggs! Can you find 4?

When it senses danger, the Sprocket Wheel Fish will inflate its body to make its prickly spines stick out. Do you dare to find 3?

It is the male Sea Horse which carries the young in its pouch. There are 6 to find, not counting the young sea horses!

26

The Stone Fish is the master of camouflage. See if you can find 6!

The Giant Squid can grow up to 18 metres.

The Blue Whale is the largest mammal in the world - 133 metres in length and weighing 130 tonnes! You can easily see 4.

Just one eye has a diameter of 39 cm! You will need to look hard to find 5!

# Animals of Oceania

Oceania is the name given to Australia, New Zealand and surrounding islands. Many animals of Oceania exist nowhere else on Earth, including marsupials – animals where the female rears her young in a body pouch.

Find 4 animals – the first is a thief, the second miaows, the third bleats, the fourth neighs.

At 1.5 m high, the Cassowary can be dangerous to humans because of its large claws. Take care searching for 8!

Most unusual about the Marsupial Mouse is its eyes – it doesn't have any! Open your eyes and you will see 5!

The Duck-billed Platypus is a mammal – but it lays eggs, has a duck's bill, feeds its

At birth, young kangaroos are only 2 cm long and weigh 1 gramme. Can you find 4 adults?

own milk, and digs tunnels! See if you can find 7!

When danger threatens, the Spiny Anteater can bury itself within a few seconds. Hurry up and find 6!

Koala means 'that which does not drink' – and it's true! That is why it rarely needs to come down from a tree. So, climb up to find 7!